# What Do We Know About Comparing Materials?

1 Draw a picture of your bedroom.

2 Label two of the materials.

3 Describe how these two materials look and feel.

_____
_____

4 Fill in the table with materials with similar and different properties.

| Material 1 | Material 2 | Similar property | Different property |
|---|---|---|---|
| glass | wood | hard | dull |
| rubber | | | |
| fur | | | |

# Describing and Comparing Materials

1. Look at this list of materials. Describe how each one looks and feels.

| Material | Look | Feel |
|---|---|---|
| Wood | brown | rough |
| Metal | | |
| Plastic | | |
| Towelling | | |
| Sponge | | |
| Cotton wool | | |
| Brick | | |
| Rock | | |

## Comparing Materials

**2a  Draw a collection of sharp objects.**

**2b  Name something that could *not* go in the collection. Explain why.**

**3a  Draw a collection of flexible objects.**

**3b  Name something that could *not* go in the collection. Explain why.**

# Exploring Soft Materials

1a Draw and label two of your toys that are made from soft materials.

1b Draw and label two of your toys that are made from hard materials.

# Comparing Materials

Here are three different types of stuffing:

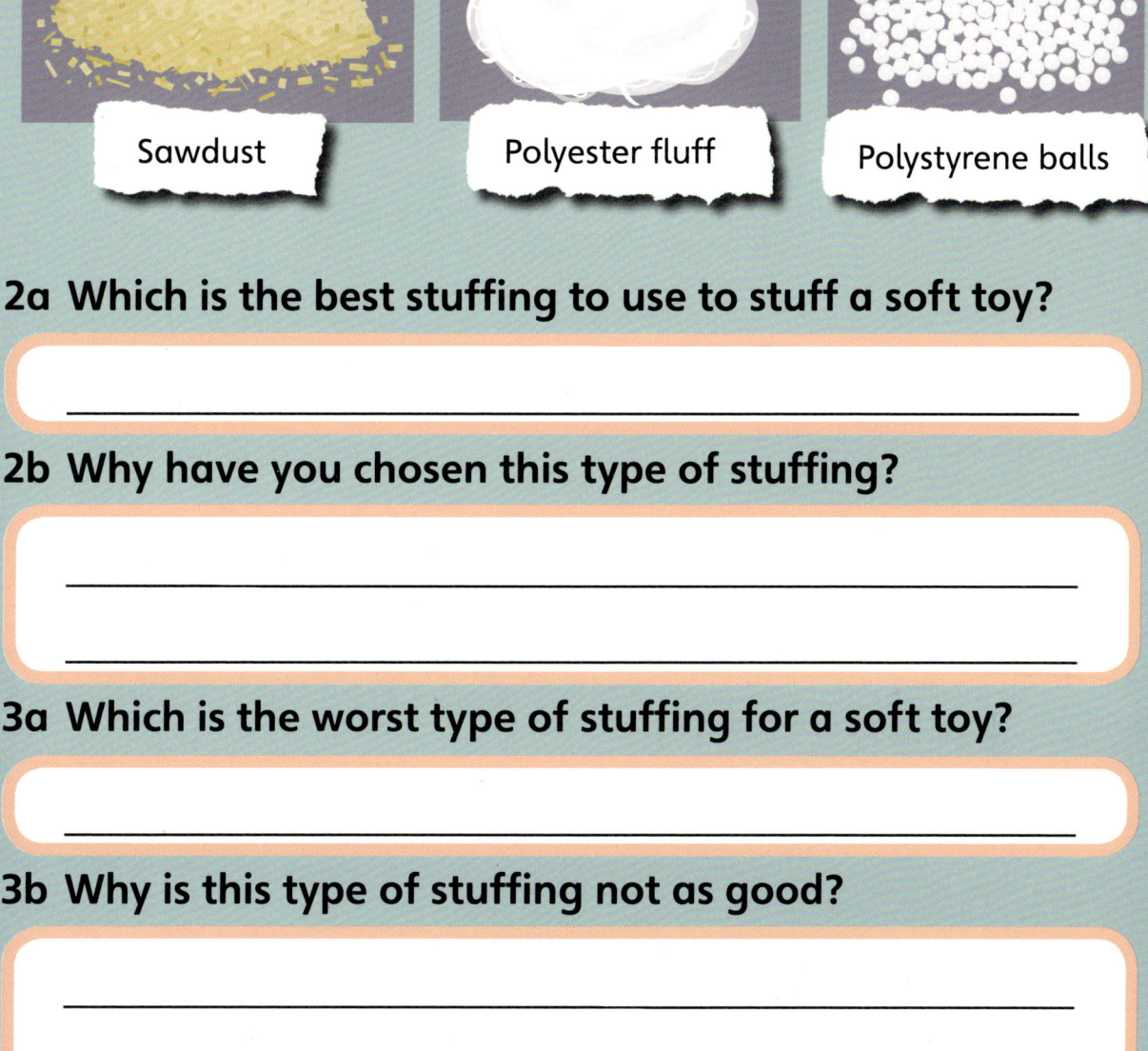

Sawdust    Polyester fluff    Polystyrene balls

**2a** Which is the best stuffing to use to stuff a soft toy?

_____

**2b** Why have you chosen this type of stuffing?

_____
_____

**3a** Which is the worst type of stuffing for a soft toy?

_____

**3b** Why is this type of stuffing not as good?

_____
_____

# Comparing Old and Modern Teddy Bears

1. Make a poster showing how a modern teddy bear is made. You can write and draw pictures. Include information about which materials are used and why they are chosen.

## Comparing Materials

**2** List three different materials that modern teddy bear eyes are made from. Draw the eyes and record which material they are made from.

| Teddy bear eyes | Material |
|---|---|
|  |  |
|  |  |
|  |  |

**3** Look at pictures of teddies that are not covered in fur. Draw one you like. Explain why.

# Design a Sock Creature

1. Design and make a sock creature. You can make your creature using scissors, glue, a sock, stuffing, felt, wool and stick-on eyes.

   Draw and label what you use for each part of your sock creature.

# Science Skills

## Classify it!

Wooden doll

Plastic doll

Rag doll

Knitted doll

China doll

1  Find two different ways of classifying these dolls into two groups. Record which dolls are in each group and say why.

| Group 1: | Group 2: |
|---|---|
|  |  |
|  |  |
|  |  |
|  |  |

# Exploring Slime

Different types of slime can have different properties.

1   Identify one of the slimes you explored. Describe its properties in three words.

_____    _____    _____

Choose another slime.

**2a** How is it similar to the first slime?

_____

**2b** How is it different from the first slime?

_____

3   Classify some slimes into two groups.

| Group 1: | Group 2: |
|---|---|
|  |  |
|  |  |
|  |  |
|  |  |

# Science Skills

## Observe it!

If a ball of slime is left on a saucer it will change.

1. How do you think a thick, sticky slime will change? Draw your ideas in the table below.

| At first | After a minute | After a week |
|---|---|---|
|  |  |  |

2. How do you think a thin, runny slime will change? Draw your ideas in the table below.

| At first | After a minute | After a week |
|---|---|---|
|  |  |  |

# Science Skills

## Test it!

1. How would you test to find out whether these different types of cloths sink in water? Draw each step of what you would do.

**Comparing Materials**

2  Using the cloths and a bowl of water, test to find out whether each cloth sinks. Record your results in the table.

| Type of cloth | Test result |
|---|---|
| Dish | |
| Microfibre | |
| Sponge | |
| Flannel | |

3  Record three things you found out.

1 _____

2 _____

3 _____

# Transparent, Opaque or Translucent?

1. Do you think metal foil is transparent, opaque or translucent?

   _____

2. Do you think cling film is transparent, opaque or translucent?

   _____

3. Do you think greaseproof paper is transparent, opaque or translucent?

   _____

4. Which other materials do you predict will be transparent, opaque and translucent? List two for each in the table.

| Transparent materials | Opaque materials | Translucent materials |
|---|---|---|
|  |  |  |

# Comparing Materials

We can use a torch to find out which materials are transparent, opaque and translucent.

5   Test metal foil, cling film, greaseproof paper and the materials you listed on page 14. Record your findings in the table below.

| Transparent materials | Opaque materials | Translucent materials |
|---|---|---|
|  |  |  |

# What Have We Learned About Different Materials?

1. Look at the properties in the table below. List a material that has the property. List a material that does *not* have the property.

| Property | Material that has the property | Material that does *not* have the property |
|---|---|---|
| Hard | | |
| Shiny | | |
| Stretchy | | |
| Floats in water | | |
| Transparent | | |

2. Classify these craft materials into two groups.

cardboard, cellophane, paper, tissue, glitter, foil, dough, wool

Group 1:

Group 2:

## INTERNATIONAL

Fuel curiosity, spark imagination.

| UK National Curriculum YEAR 1 | CAMBRIDGE primary Stages 1, 3 | Pearson iPRIMARY YEAR 1, 2 |

*Science Bug International* is an exciting and comprehensive science programme that has been designed to make sure your children never stop asking questions about their world!

This Workbook contains questions from the Topic Book plus additional questions to reinforce and extend learning.

With full and comprehensive coverage of the skills and knowledge required for curriculum attainment, *Science Bug International* will help you to nurture and inspire your young scientist.

Series editor: Deborah Herridge
Author: Debbie Eccles

www.pearsonschools.co.uk
myorders@pearson.com

ISBN 978-0-435-19558-8